PINT-SIZE SCIENCE

Finding-Out Fun for You and Your Young Child

by Linda Allison and Martha Weston

Little, Brown and Company

Boston   New York   Toronto   London

The authors thank the moms, dads, aunts, uncles, teachers, librarians, and kids who generously shared their ideas, stories, and experience for this book.

A special thanks to Marvin Wolfe and the kids and staff at the San Anselmo Preschool; Tracy Williams, Ethel Seiderman, and the kids and staff at the Fairfax–San Anselmo Children's Center; Peggy Dodge; and Barbara Young.

A very special thanks to Patricia Monighan Nourot, Ph.D., Professor of Early Childhood Education at Sonoma State University, for guiding the content and adding her ideas, humor, and expert review.

FIRST EDITION

10 9 8 7 6 5 4 3 2 1

IM

Published simultaneously in Canada by Little, Brown & Company (Canada) Limited

The Brown Paper Preschool books are edited and prepared for publication at The Yolla Bolly Press, Covelo, California, under the supervision of James and Carolyn Robertson. Editorial and production staff: Renee Menge, Diana Fairbanks, and Alexandra Chappell. Composition by Wilsted & Taylor, Oakland.

Library of Congress Cataloging-in-Publication Data

Allison, Linda.
    Pint-size science : finding-out fun for you and your young child / Linda Allison and Martha Weston.
        p.   cm. — (A Brown paper preschool book)
        ISBN 0-316-03467-3
        1. Science—Study and teaching (Preschool)
    2. Education, Preschool—Activity programs.
    I. Weston, Martha.   II. Title.   III. Series.
    LB1140.5.S35A44   1994
    372.3—dc20   93-38557

Printed in Hong Kong

★ CONTENTS ★

ABOUT THIS BOOK **5**

LOOKING LIKE A SCIENTIST

LEARNING NOTES: Nobody Knows It All **6**
Walk and Talk: sensing and sorting the everyday world **7**
Collections: sorting out and showing off collected treasures **9**
Smellers, Shakers, and Feelies: games for the senses **10**

SOLIDS, LIQUIDS, GASES

LEARNING NOTES: Scientific Method for the Very Young **12**
Wind Ring: make an outdoor wind detector **13**
Go Blow Air!: put air to work pushing things around **14**
Bubble Lab: testing and stretching soap film **16**
Water and Sand Play: measuring and pouring **18**
Float a Boat: experimenting with sink or float **20**
Juicy Cubes: making mixtures and freezing treats to eat **21**
Cooking Up Chemistry: simple science you can eat **22**

ENERGY AND LIGHT

LEARNING NOTES: Helping Your Child Think **24**
Static Magic: exploring static electricity **25**
Messing with Magnets: playing with an invisible force **26**
Marble Mazes: fun with rolling and falling **28**
Bouncing Beams: messing around with mirrors **30**
Shadow Tracks: sunny day play **31**

PLANTS

LEARNING NOTES: Using Science to Sort Out Life **32**
Dandy Dandelions: observing flying seeds and plant parts **33**
Seeds, Please!: take a seed safari around the house **34**
Magic Beans: plant babies inside and out **36**

ANIMALS

LEARNING NOTES: Making Friends with Animals **38**
Pet Parts: a hands-on anatomy lesson **39**
Bugs?: leg counts and discovering animal differences **40**
Pill Bugs: one very common critter up close **41**
Wild Kingdom: meet ladybugs, earthworms, and snails **42**
Animal House: observing and making critter habitats **44**

SKILLS LIST

Basic skills defined **46**

INDEX

An activity guide sorted by place **48**

Where's the "ology"?

Biology, geology, zoology, and chemistry—they're all here. We just don't call them that, because your kid doesn't either. Preschoolers like their science hands-on, without fancy labels. For that, you've come to the right place!

★ ABOUT THIS BOOK ★

Your preschooler is probably crazy about science. She wants to know why Jell-O wiggles and why water is wet. She is simply fascinated by these questions and a million others. If you're like most adults, though, your memory of science as it was taught in school makes you a little uneasy. It conjures up bad smells in biology or the terror of a physics exam. The difference between your preschooler and you is that she doesn't call it science. You don't have to either. Think of it as discovery, pure and simple.

The science in this book will help you and your preschooler to discover the world. The activities are designed to be easy and fun, using things from around the house.

Some activities bring a science slant to what you already do (such as making a melted cheese sandwich or taking a bath or a walk). Some activities are portable. Others are designed as open-ended play labs for experimenting with simple things such as magnets or bubbles.

Don't be alarmed if you don't have access to the exact items listed in each activity or if the exact materials don't suit your child. If your kid hates pill bugs but loves grasshoppers, just borrow the approach and substitute your kid's preferred bug. All the activities are written in a general way so that they can be easily adapted. Remember, anything can be science. And don't forget to have fun. Who knows, you just might get excited about science yourself.

Dad, Dad, can we take dis sand to our house?

Look! My hands disdapeared!

I found a rock!

★ NOBODY KNOWS IT ALL ★

Little ones bombard you with a constant stream of questions: "Where did this come from?" "How come?" "How did it get here?" "Why is it like that?" "What happens if . . . ?"

These are exactly the same kinds of questions that scientists ask. What is interesting is that both kids and scientists are comfortable with having a lot more questions than answers.

Scientists know that if you ask why, you often run into a blank wall. The truth is, so far, nobody really knows why lemmings jump into the sea or what holds the universe together. Not really. Not ultimately.

So what's this got to do with you and your preschooler?

It means you can relax. If scientists don't know all the answers, then you certainly can't expect to. Just know that the way to an answer lies in asking many questions. In the process we learn how to ask better questions that eventually enable us to get at some of the answers.

When it comes to science, do what preschoolers and particle physicists do: get comfortable not knowing *all* the answers and just enjoy the wonder.

★ WALK AND TALK ★

"Oh, look!" "Can I pet the kitty?" "What's that man doing?" "Phew, smell this!" Little ones know how to become absorbed in everything they encounter. This can be infuriating if you're in a hurry . . . so don't hurry.

Walk and Talk. Let your kid be the guide. Slow down to a child's pace. Look, listen, smell, and touch whatever you find along the way. Do this in the woods, on Main Street, in a department store, or in your backyard.

Theme Walk. Walk with a mission.
- "Hey, Kate! Let's go out and look for seeds" (or stones or leaves or bugs).
- "Let's count cars" (or cats or cracks).
- "Let's look for yellow things" (or red things).
- "Let's find puddles." (Rain boots for this!)

What Sort Walk. Little kids are born collectors. Set out with a bag or backpack for carrying home treasures. At home, empty the collected items onto a towel or newspaper. Talk about your finds:

- "What do you like the best? . . . What's the smallest? . . . The hardest?"
- "Let's sort. What kinds of piles could we make?"

  white/not-white things
  metal/nonmetal things
  things that grow/don't grow

- Invent categories. (One child we know decided to arrange items from most alive to most dead.) The complexity will increase as your child's skill grows.

  Animal, mineral, or vegetable?
  Two legs, four legs, more legs?

Whole World Series. Sticks, leaves, stones, or shells are all you need to play this game. Simply sort items from big to little, little to big, or dark to light. Use any serial combination that makes sense.

Sorting and Classifying. Put a very young child down with a pile of objects, and she will naturally begin sorting and grouping. A preschooler loves to classify. She naturally asks, "What's different? What's the same?" It may look like child's play, but your kid is exploring an important tool for discovery. Scientists ask these same simple "What's different? What's the same?" questions to discover new information about subjects as complex as viruses or stars.

★ COLLECTIONS ★

Show off your child's collected treasures. Organizing sticks, stones, leaves, seeds, feathers, and shells can be a delightful lesson in logic.

Stick-ups. A simple strip of tape makes a display for lightweight treasures. Even the tiniest kid can use this method.

Tack tape to window or bulletin board.

Museum in a Box. When it comes time to clean up, save the best specimens and toss the rest. Let your child choose and sort them into the appropriate bag.

Ziploc bags

shoebox
LEAVES
STONES
SHELLS
STICKS

COLLECTOR CARDS

Organizing treasures collected from a walk or a trip to the beach can be a sorting activity. Glue the sorted groups to cards. Label. Hang them up. How about . . .

Look! Another fuzzy seed!

SEED WALK

MOM'S SUE'S

Blue things
Red things
Green things
Brown things

COLOR HIKE

GRAPH YOUR STUFF				
Leaves				4
Rocks				2
Seeds				7
Odds and Ends				3

★ SMELLERS, SHAKERS, AND FEELIES ★

Smellers is a guessing game for the nose, Shakers is for the ears, and Feelies for the fingers. Playing these games sharpens the senses and stretches the memory, whatever your age. Film cans are often free from your photo shop.

TO MAKE SMELLERS

Snap the lids onto several empty plastic film cannisters. Poke several holes in each lid with the tip of a sharp knife.

Fill pairs of cans with cotton balls that are scented with perfume or with peppermint or vanilla flavoring. Or try bits of:
onion
orange
cloves
cinnamon
chocolate
lemon

Make a Match. To start, put samples of each item in the cans out on a table. Invite your child to find matching cans by using his nose.
HARDER: Guess the contents of a can by using only your nose.

I know! It smells like spaghetti!

TO MAKE SHAKERS

Fill a pair of plastic film cannisters with one of the following materials:
rice
paper clips
washers
toothpicks
marbles
salt
water
cotton balls
nothing at all

Snap the lids on tight. Make more pairs of shakers using other materials from the list. Eight pairs is a good number to start with.

Both of these are rocks.

Make a Match. Set out the shakers. Mix them up. Give one a shake. "Hey, Chris, can you find another can that sounds like this one?"

What's Inside? Set out several shakers with different contents. "Can you guess what's inside? . . . Which ones are empty? . . . How do you know?"

This one is loud. I think it's marbles.

TO MAKE A FEELIE BOX

Cut the foot off a large tube sock. Stretch the tube section over the opening of a small round oatmeal box.

Fool Me. Invite your child to set up the Feelie Box to see if she can fool you.

Pull Out. Pile a number of items into the Feelie Box. "Can you pull out the key? The ring? No fair peeking!"

Make a Match. Put several matching things into the Feelie Box. "Pull something out. Can you find another that's the same?"

That one's slippery.

Oh, this is scratchy. I think I got another pretzel.

Guess What?
1. Secretly put one item in the box.
2. "Laura, ready to feel? Tell me what it feels like. Soft? Hard? Smooth? Bumpy? Cold? Round? Pointy?"
3. "What do you think it is? A button? Let's see if you were right." Don't forget to talk while you go along—it's half the fun.

★ SCIENTIFIC METHOD FOR THE VERY YOUNG ★

Teddy Bear took a bath because Jenny wanted to know if he could swim. *Thunk!* A truck flew off the deck because Derek wanted to see if it would crash. Preschoolers are always testing the world around them, though few would think of their testing as "scientific."

All of us, even kids, use this guess-and-test method, but usually in an informal way. At the core of science is a way of thinking called the "scientific method." These are the steps:

1. Observation: "Wow! Ants are having a party in the kitchen."
2. Prediction (also called a hypothesis): "They must be attracted to the garbage can."

3. Test: "Let's take out the garbage can and see if the ants disappear."
4. Conclusion: "The ants are gone. They were after the garbage."

The next time your kid asks you one of those endless "whys," see if together you can't apply some scientific thinking. Don't expect little ones to suddenly become step-by-step thinkers. They are much too impetuous for that. But gradually they will learn that sometimes they can answer their own questions. It's a powerful feeling.

★ WIND RING ★

A wind ring is fun to look at and easy to make. Hang it outside and watch the wind push it around. Fast or slow? Where does the wind come from? Where does it go? Watching the wind leads naturally to talk about the weather.

You will need:
wide-mouth plastic lid
large plastic bags or
    colored ribbons
string

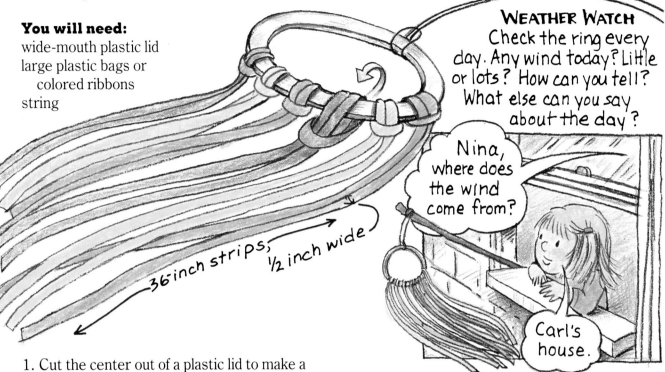

36-inch strips; ½ inch wide

WEATHER WATCH
Check the ring every day. Any wind today? Little or lots? How can you tell? What else can you say about the day?

Nina, where does the wind come from?

Carl's house.

1. Cut the center out of a plastic lid to make a ring.
2. Cut half-inch strips of plastic or ribbon about a yard long.
3. Loop the strips around the ring. (Your child will need help learning how.) You will need about a dozen strips.
4. Loop on a string for hanging.
5. When it's done, your child will naturally want to take it out and run it around to make it fly.
6. Hang the wind ring outside a window, where you can see it blow in the breeze.

Streamer. A long paper streamer or scarf outside on a windy day can be great fun to trail around. Make it twist and turn.

★ GO BLOW AIR! ★

Introduce your child to air while waiting for the food to come at a restaurant. All it takes is a straw. As you might have guessed, it is even better to do this full-blown activity at home, where you can really test a straw's limits.

You will need:
plastic straws
Ziploc bag
odd bits (washers, pencils, paper tubes,
    bottle caps)

3. Pull out the straw and zip the bag shut, holding in the air.
4. "What color is air? Where did it come from? Can you feel it? Can you blow it away?"

Straw Play. "What can you do with a straw? Drink? What else? Blow your hair? Make bubbles? Tickle? Any other ideas?"

Air Bag. You can't see air, but it's really there. Catch some in a bag to prove it.
1. Zip a straw into a Ziploc bag, leaving one end of the straw sticking out.
2. "What do you think will happen when you blow? Let's try."

Blow...

Pull out straw. Zip shut.

There's your air!

Blow or No? Guess and test a handful of heavy and lightweight objects such as washers, pencils, paper tubes, and bottle caps.

1. "Hey, Sam, want to make a prediction? Can you guess which things will move when you blow on them and which ones won't?"
2. "Let's make two piles: yes and no."
3. "Let's test with the straws."

These are the YES blowy things and these are the NOs.

Hint: Learning how to guess and test is the point, not necessarily making correct predictions. Younger children will be happy to simply test by blowing the lightweight things around.

Race. You need at least two racers. Each picks out something to blow. Set up a raceway on the floor or on a tabletop. Mark the start and the finish lines with tape. Ready, set, blow!

Let's play a blowing game. You blow it to me. I'll blow it back.

And no fair if it falls off the table.

Look! It blows out the back!

★ BUBBLE LAB ★

Wiggle, jiggle, pop! Blow bubbles outdoors on the wind or indoors on a tabletop. Either way, bubble making offers lots of opportunity for experimenting and plenty of fooling-around fun. Children of all ages adore bubbles.

You will need:
bubble soap (homemade or store-bought)
cups
plastic straws

Set up an indoor bubble lab in an easy-to-clean place. Work on a smooth, washable tabletop or counter or tray.

Bubble Cup. Even tiny kids can blow a pile of bubbles this way. Pour about half an inch of bubble soap into a small cup. Put the straw into the soap. Blow. Don't suck!

> **Bubble Soap:** To make your own, mix:
> 5 cups cool water
> ½ cup dishwashing liquid
>
> Add a few drops of glycerine for longer-lasting bubbles.

Big Bubble. By now the table should be wet. Dip a straw into the soap. Place it flat on the wet table and blow slowly.
- Can you make a big bubble?
- Two stuck together?
- One inside another?

Bubble Questions. Younger children will be content to blow piles of bubbles and to pop them. To get their minds involved, ask some think-about-it questions such as:

- What color is a bubble?
- Can you touch a bubble without making it pop? (The secret is a wet finger.)

Tricky Bubbles. Kids with more coordination might try making:

- **Bubble Chains**
- **Double Domes**
- **Wiggle Worms**

Hint: Bubbles last longer in humid, damp weather than on dry days.

Outdoor Bubbles. All sorts of things can be used to blow bubbles. Pour about an inch of bubble soap into a wide bowl. Round up a selection of bubble makers. Take all the tools outside for a backyard bubble lab.

Wands. Children like to bend their own bubble wands from pipe cleaners. Before they start to blow, ask them to guess what shape bubbles each wand will make.

★ WATER AND SAND PLAY ★

Plunk a preschooler down in a bathtub or a sandbox and he becomes an instant scientist. Pouring, measuring, and experimenting with sand can keep a kid busy for hours. Playing where sand and water come together is even better!

You will need:

unbreakable containers of many shapes and
  sizes: measuring cups, scoops, spoons, bags,
  saucers, throwaway cartons, pots, pans, pails,
  funnels, plastic tubing (from the hardware
  store)
basters
sieves

Bathtub Play. The bathtub is a natural spot for water play. All a child really needs to get started testing the waters is a bucket of containers within easy reach.

Sand Play. Almost all the activities that are appropriate for water play work with sand, too. Give your child scoops and containers for digging and molding.

Other Water Places. A wading pool, the kitchen sink (with a stool), or a dishpan on a table with a towel to catch the mess—all make fine places for water play. Add suds or food coloring to the water for fun. Plastic toys invite all sorts of pretend play.

Try asking:
- "How many cups of water will fit in that pot? Can you guess? Let's count."
- "I bet that big fat cup won't fill this skinny glass. What do you think?"
- "What will happen if you stick the tube under the water and blow?"

★ FLOAT A BOAT ★

Sink or float? Many things can be made into a boat. Try some nautical engineering with your child. Making boats while bathing can be good, clean scientific fun.

You will need:
water in a bath, wading pool, or big dishpan
sinkers and floaters: corks, twist ties, rubber
    bands, Styrofoam containers, pennies, bottle
    caps, plastic lids, keys, washers
aluminum foil
plastic straw

Sink or Float? Set up a water play place. Then spread out some sinkers and floaters. Talk about them. "Kevin, do you guess this would make a boat?" Sort the items into a sink pile and a float pile. Test to find out.

Build a Boat. Small sheets of aluminum foil make an easy boat. Turn up the edges. Test it in water to see how it floats. What else does it need? Try combining different materials to make a boat.

Passengers. "Do you think your boat can take a passenger?" Add a bottle cap or penny. "How many can it take?" Predictions, please. "Which boat can take the most? How can we find out?"

Whoa!
It sinks!

Sail a Boat. Push those boats around with a blast of air through a straw. "Want to race?"

SCIENCE WORDS: *SINK, FLOAT, PREDICT*

★ JUICY CUBES ★

Making mixtures, blending colors and flavors, melting solids, freezing liquids, and taste testing—the kitchen can be the liveliest science lab around.

You will need:
fruit juices (bright-colored juices such as grape,
  fruit punch, and orange work best)
small pitchers
plastic ice cube tray
eyedropper or baster

1. Pour juices into small pitchers. (If you use frozen juice, invite your child to help mix them.)
2. Set out the ice cube tray and juices. "Sean, want to make some fruit cubes?"
3. Demonstrate pouring. "Not too full."
4. Predict what will happen when you mix flavors. "What will orange and grape make?" "Gorange?"
5. Fill the tray and set it in the freezer. "What do you think will happen next?"

To Eat. After they're frozen, empty the cubes into a bowl. Wrap a cube in a paper towel when you're ready for a snack. Suck them up.

To Drink. Set several glasses out with different-colored cubes in each. "What do you think will happen to the cubes out of the freezer?" "When should we come back to check?" Predict the flavors based on the colors.

SKILLS: PREDICTING, TRANSFORMATION, REVERSIBILITY   SCIENCE WORDS: *SOLID, LIQUID, MELTING, FREEZING* **21**

★ COOKING UP CHEMISTRY ★

A lot of chemistry happens in most homes every day of the week. We call it cooking. Any food preparation can be science when you invite your kid to measure, mix, and predict. Get started with some cinnamon toast.

Cinnamon Toast
You will need:
sugar
ground cinnamon
butter or margarine
bread slices

1. Invite your child to smell and feel the sugar and cinnamon. Talk about the tastes and textures. Explore with all your senses.
2. Show your child how to measure three teaspoons of sugar and one teaspoon of cinnamon. Pour them into a container that has a lid.

3. "Kay, can you predict what will happen if you give them a shake? (Oops, don't forget the lid!) Look, you made a mixture!"
4. Blend the butter and the cinnamon sugar together. "How can we do this?"
5. Spread the butter on toast. "We could eat it like this, but what would happen if we put it back in the toaster oven? Want to see?"

Experiment: Some people like cinnamon spread on untoasted bread. Others sprinkle the ingredients separately. What's your favorite recipe?

For More Science Fun. Try cooking up these dissolving, melting, freezing, or exploding foods. Notice the changes that happen as you cook. Talk about what caused them.

Jell-O
popcorn
dried fruit or fruit leather
frozen bananas
melted cheese sandwiches

☆ Dip bananas in melted chocolate. Stick in a fork.

FREEZE.

☆ MELT cheese on open-faced sandwiches in oven or microwave.

☆ EXPLODE some popcorn. Grate on cheese. Let it MELT.

Yum!

TRANSFORMATIONS

Things change. Ice melts. Water evaporates. A lump of cookie dough can be divided into bits. The bits can be squished back into a big lump. (This is a "reversible transformation.") Bake the cookie dough, and watch the cookies become dry and hard. Can they be changed back? No. (This is a "nonreversible transformation.") Children need many experiences to learn about the different ways the world changes. Cooking is a wonderful way to explore change.

Two dough balls.

Now they's all mooshed up!

REVERSIBLE

Two cookies.

They don't moosh together.

Except in my mouth!

NONREVERSIBLE

★ HELPING YOUR CHILD THINK ★

The best learning happens when kids are given plenty of room to test things out for themselves in a free-form, playful way. Many of the projects in this book are designed to take advantage of the fact that to little kids, the whole world is a science lab. You supply the materials, then step out of the way and let your kid experiment and play.

Does this mean get out and stay out? No. Often you can step in and offer a suggestion, or ask a question that will help your child solve a problem or send her off experimenting in a whole new way.

How do you know when to step in and when to keep out of the way? You don't. Knowing when to lead and when to let your kid follow her own instincts is an art. It takes years to master. You will still be struggling with this question when your child is in college. No matter. As long as you don't squash her curiosity or crowd out her initiative, you're doing fine.

Hint: Be stingy with "right" answers. Draw her into thinking out loud. (Besides, you can probably use this thinking time to wash a few dishes or feed the baby.) Challenge your child to invent her own answers with these kinds of questions:

Why do you suppose . . . ?
I wonder if . . . ?
How can we find out?

What do you think will happen next?
What now?
Does it always happen?
Try it and see.
What do you think will happen when . . . ?

Invite your child to be the captain on her own voyages of discovery. Let her choose the direction. Take a backseat and enjoy the ride.

★ STATIC MAGIC ★

Some parents swear their kids have extra energy on dry, windy days. Indeed, there is electricity in the air. It's a perfect sort of day for investigating static magic.

Dancing Bits Bottle
You will need:

lightweight paper (tissue is best)
clear plastic box or plastic liter bottle
silk or wool cloth

1. Cut a handful of tiny paper bits. Cut some tiny people while your kid snips confetti-sized bits.
2. Pour the paper bits into the plastic container and close the lid.
3. Rub the plastic surface with the silk or wool. Watch the bits inside hop around as the surface gets charged.

I maked the guys dance!

Things to Try

- Listen. "Do you hear anything when you rub?"
- Take off the lid. Hold the box upside-down. "What makes the bits stick?"
- Pull papers away. Let them go.
- Salt or sugar also "dances" nicely.

Balloon Tricks

Blow up a balloon. Rub the surface with silk or wool until it's charged.

- Let it pick up bits of paper.
- Arrange the bits to make a face.
- Can you create enough electricity to stick the balloon to the wall? Or to you?

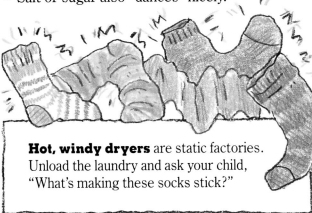

Hot, windy dryers are static factories. Unload the laundry and ask your child, "What's making these socks stick?"

Rub up a charge.

Paper bits hop on (attract).

Make a face with the bits.

Look! It's sticking to me!

★ MESSING WITH MAGNETS ★

Magnets are clean, neat, forgiving, and fun. Tell a preschooler why magnets work, and he won't remember. But give the same kid a magnet and time to explore, and the child will begin to get a real feel for how magnets work.

You will need:
magnets (Collect them from grocery, toy, and
   stationery supply stores.)

Explore. Give your child the magnets and a selection of odds and ends, such as paper clips, bottle caps, keys, coins, and plastic items. Let your child explore.

Try Asking: "Did the magnet pick up a wood chip, the paper, a bottle cap? What things did it pick up? What doesn't it lift?" Eventually, your child will notice magnets lift certain metals. Don't rush to explain.

Guess and Test. "Do you think a magnet will stick to the fridge? How about the sink? The TV?" Travel around the house guessing and testing. **WARNING:** Keep magnets away from all computer equipment, TV screens, and credit cards!

Mighty Magnet. Find out which magnet is the strongest. Which pulls the most clips? Count to find out.

Flying Clip Trick. Tie a paper clip to a length of thread. Tape the thread to the table. Lift the clip with a magnet. How far away can you place the magnet without dropping the clip?

Backseat science is possible if you have a magnet along for the ride. Test where it sticks in the car or wherever you visit on a trip.

Pushy Power. Two bar magnets can attract or repel. Hold two magnets together and feel their pushy (repelling) force. Tape one onto a toy car. Hold the other and push the car around.

SEE A MAGNET'S INVISIBLE POWER

Use a rough metal file on a big steel nail to make iron filings. Sprinkle iron filings on paper. Invite your child to slide a strong magnet under the paper to see a picture of the magnet's force.

Dancing Pins. Put a handful of pins and clips on a stiff card. Move the magnet under the card. Can a magnet pull through a card? Does it work through a book? A table? Your hand? Water? Experiment.

★ MARBLE MAZES ★

Zooming marbles are lots of fun. The setup is simple. These mazes offer many lessons: a feel for the physics of falling (inclines and speed) and, of course, lots of practice stacking and building. It's good for a group, but enticing enough alone. Save those tubes. Your kid will want to play again and again.

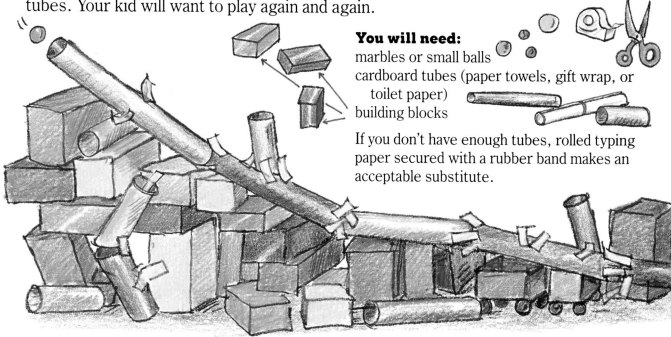

You will need:
marbles or small balls
cardboard tubes (paper towels, gift wrap, or
    toilet paper)
building blocks

If you don't have enough tubes, rolled typing paper secured with a rubber band makes an acceptable substitute.

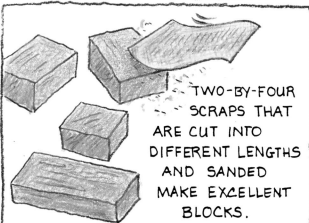

TWO-BY-FOUR SCRAPS THAT ARE CUT INTO DIFFERENT LENGTHS AND SANDED MAKE EXCELLENT BLOCKS.

Begin with a single marble, a tube, and a few blocks.
1. Build a simple incline. "Mikey, what do you think would happen if I dropped a marble here? Watch." "Cool. Lemme try."

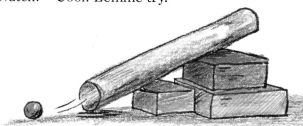

2. Add some more tubes and marbles. Step out of the way. Invite your child to play with making his own marble tracks.

"It's a chimbly!"

"Don't move, Pickle."

Here it comes!

Try Asking:
- "Can you make the marble go faster?"
- "What happens if you start lower?"
- "How far can a marble go?"
- "Can you make a marble catcher?"

3. Add new items from time to time. Try different kinds of balls. Split some of the tubes. Tape tubes together for long runs.

Do you think those will fit?

MARBLE ALERT: DON'T TRY THIS IF YOUR KID IS TOO YOUNG TO KEEP THE MARBLES OUT OF HIS MOUTH.

★ BOUNCING BEAMS ★

Mirrors are magic. They can catch a light beam and bounce it around on your toe, up on a wall, or on the ground. They're a simple way to play with cause and effect. All you need is a sunny day and two small mirrors.

1. Show your child how to catch the sun on the mirror and shoot it onto a wall.
2. Move it around. "Where is it now?"
3. "Want to try?"

Hint: Start close to a wall. It will take a bit of practice before a child sees how moving his hand moves the spot of light.

Light Drawing. Tape up a big piece of paper on a shadowed wall within your kid's reach. Reflect the beam around the paper. Invite your preschooler to trace the beam's path with a fat marker.

1 There it is!

It's like Tinkerbell.

2 I did it!

Great! Can you bounce it on the door?

On the floor?

In the window?

3 Try to make it touch my chin.

Careful. It's too bright to shine in my eyes.

Does it tickle?

4 Can you put your spot on mine?

I catched yours!

5 How far can it go? How close? Can it go up? Down? All around?

Now it's gone. Wait, it's back!

6 Hey! Where's the light?

Why won't it work at night?

Or on a cloudy day?

SCIENCE WORDS: *LIGHT BEAM, REFLECTING*

★ SHADOW TRACKS ★

Who follows you all around? Who's your faithful friend on the ground? Who does what you do? Your shadow—that's who! Why not get acquainted? Draw a picture of your shadow friend.

Shadow Me
You will need:
chalk
smooth pavement
sunny day

1. "Look, your shadow does what you do. Can you make it hop? Wiggle? Fly? Can you make a really silly shadow?"
2. Trace your child's shadow. Draw around the feet. Talk as you draw. "Neck. Now where am I? Head."
3. "Now, you do my shadow." Let your child trace.

- Do a series of crazy poses. Write your name in each one.
- Can you fit back in your shadow outline?
- Where are the eyes? Shadows don't have eyes, but you can draw them in.

SHADOW MAP
Trace the path of the shifting sun, or just trace shapes for some drawing fun.
1. Tape a simple paper shape onto a sunny window.
2. Put a large sheet of paper on the floor to catch the shadow shape.
3. At intervals during the day, come back and trace the shape. "What happens to the shadow? Why won't it hold still?"
4. At the end of the day, color your shapes.

The death of a plant or a pet, an illness in the family, a fire, the birth of a baby—any big, new experience can be disturbing for a small child. Science information can help your child sort it out.

When there was a flood in town, a teacher we know noticed many anxious kids in his preschool class. In science circle he talked about the event and what the children were feeling. He also discussed soil, rain, and weather. He found these talks helped kids be less afraid in two ways. Just talking seems to help. But understanding the hows and whys of a scary event also helps kids cope.

Using science books can help children understand the world around them. The best books for young children have lots of illustrations that a child can easily understand. Books that tell stories are also very appealing to preschoolers. (If the text is too advanced, you can still use the book. Simply translate the story to language that your child will understand.)

Make reading a conversation. Ask for your child's ideas. "What do you think is happening in the picture? That may be true. What else? Why is the animal afraid? Would you be?" Encourage your child to make connections.

Inviting your child to talk about things he sees in a book lets him reveal his feelings and ideas to you in ways impossible to get to by direct questions. With that information, you'll be better able to help your child cope with any puzzling or scary event in our big and often bewildering world.

★ DANDY DANDELIONS ★

The job of flowers is to make seeds. Dandelions are unusual because they make flowers and seeds at the same time. No dandelions? Pick any flower. With a magnifying glass, the myriad shapes and parts of any flower are fascinating.

Meet the Seeds. Pull off a bit of fluff. "See the seeds? How many can you count? How do these seeds travel?"

FLOWER PARTS

stigma
stamens
petals
seed

Meet the Flowers. Every dandelion flower is actually about 200 separate flowers, and each makes its own seed. Take a yellow dandelion flower apart to see. A magnifying glass will help.

PLANT PARTS
stem
leaves
veins
roots

It makes my fingers yellow!

Guess. *Dandelion* is French for "tooth of the lion." Look at the leaves to guess why.

★ SEEDS, PLEASE! ★

It's likely baby plants are lurking around your kitchen in their seed suits, just waiting for a chance to get growing. Maybe you and your kid would like to take a seed safari or start a seedy collection? Look around indoors and out. You'll be surprised how many seeds can be found.

Inside Seeds. Go on a seed hunt inside the house. Look for them:
- on toast and bagels
- in jams, in mustard, in packages of peanuts and cereals
- inside fruit: apples, oranges, or watermelons, and on strawberries
- in soup: lima beans, lentils
- in a jewelry box: seedy necklaces
- in the middle of flowers on the table

Secret Seed. Can you find a banana seed? HINT: There is only one.

Baby beans!

Outside Seeds. Go outdoors on a seed walk (late summer and fall are the best times for seeds). Look on lawns, in weedy places, or on trees. Check your socks for sticky seeds when you get back.

Let's check.

Is that a seed?

burdock

stickers

thistle

cranberries

floaters

flyers

maple fruits

cherries

swallows (Animals eat seeds and deposit them someplace else.)

Things to Notice: Seeds Travel. It would be too crowded if all of a plant's seeds had to grow where they fell. Seeds have different tricks for traveling.

Seed Collection. Why not start a seed collection? Find a box. Put small seeds in little jars, film cannisters, or plastic bags. It's a fine project for sorting and classifying—some seeds are alike, and others are different.

★ MAGIC BEANS ★

Any seed, even a dried bean, can be magic. Just add water, and suddenly the baby plant inside breaks out of its neat package and grows into a green plant. Here's a way for your whole family to watch the magic up close.

How can de plant fit in dere?

You will need:
paper towel
glass
dried beans (big ones such as limas or favas)

Glass Garden. Roll a paper towel to fit in a clear glass. Slide the beans between the glass and the towel. Invite your child to add about an inch of water to the glass. The towel will soak up the water and keep the beans moist. After about three days, you should see your beans start to sprout.

PAPER TOWEL

DRIED BEANS

ONE INCH OF WATER

I see another bean tail!

CAN YOU SAY . . .

Stigma, stamen, stegosaurus? Your pre-schooler doesn't need a sophisticated science vocabulary. But science words are fun to say, fun to share with friends, and can be a big self-esteem booster. Science words can be helpful for sorting out differences. "No, it's an insect. See, it has six legs." Don't over-whelm your kid with too many words. Never put vocabulary before discovery and appreciation.

Meet a Seed. A seed is really a baby plant wrapped up in a tough package together with its lunch.

Soak a handful of beans overnight in warm water. When the beans are soft, split one in half. Find the parts. See the baby?

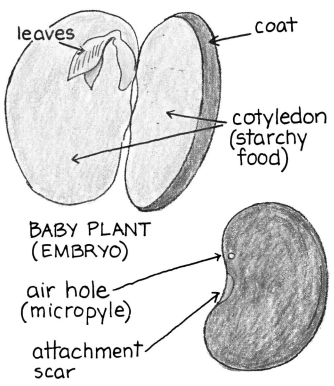

leaves

coat

cotyledon (starchy food)

BABY PLANT (EMBRYO)

air hole (micropyle)

attachment scar

Find the Hole in the Coat. Drop a few beans in boiled water, then watch for air bubbles. A tiny hole in the tough seed coat lets water in (and air out) so the bean swells and splits open its coat to grow—just as it does in the ground.

Seed Read. Whenever possible, explore an activity or idea several ways. "Jack and the Beanstalk" is a good seedy tale.

HARRY THE GARDEN
Who says science can't be a little silly? Grow some seeds and giggle as Harry sprouts a head of bright green hair. Snip some of his locks to add some color and zip to scrambled eggs or a sandwich.

You will need:
half eggshells
marker
paper ring or an eggcup
soil
alfalfa seeds

1. Draw a face on half an eggshell with a felt-tip marker.
2. Set the shell in a paper ring or eggcup.
3. Fill the shell half full of potting soil.
4. Add a pinch of seeds.
5. Fill with more soil.
6. Water, put in a warm place, and wait.

One teacher's preschool science circle is magic. Little girls are lined up, dying to hold the snakes. Small boys are petting the big, energetic iguanas. How come these kids are so fearless? Why do these creatures patiently put up with being handled by a passel of small children every day of the week?

The answer is trust. This teacher creates a caring, calm atmosphere both for the children and for the animals. His secret? Teaching his kids both a healthy caution and an enthusiasm for connecting with creatures. Here are some guidelines for you to share with your child:

It's OK to touch animals and to look at them.

Be gentle and don't hurt animals. Kids need to know they are much bigger and stronger than most animals. "Would you jump on a new friend you just met at the swings? No. You might scare him."

Don't touch any animal you don't know or are not sure about. First, ask an adult. Some animals can bite or harm you. A child may brag, "I'm not afraid of rattlesnakes." Let your child know that sometimes it's smart to be afraid. "Rattlesnakes are poison. I don't go near them because I can get hurt, too. Everybody needs to be careful."

How you act is a million times more important than what you say to a child. Attitude is everything. But what if YOU are afraid of picking up frogs? Ask yourself, Is this really a dangerous and dirty animal, or am I allowing my prejudice to interfere with my child's enjoyment of nature? If you can learn to see all creatures through your child's eyes, your child's sense of wonder just might get you past your fear.

★ PET PARTS ★

Naming body parts is fun. Play it with your family pets to make it a hands-on lesson in comparative anatomy. "Hey, Susanna, can you find your tail?"

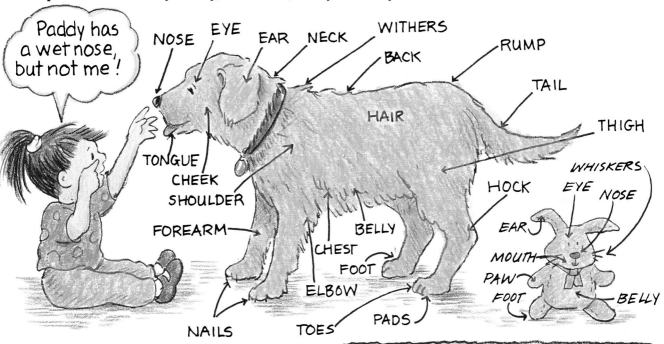

Paddy has a wet nose, but not me!

NOSE EYE EAR NECK WITHERS RUMP
BACK TAIL
HAIR THIGH
TONGUE WHISKERS
CHEEK EYE NOSE
SHOULDER HOCK
FOREARM EAR
BELLY MOUTH
CHEST PAW
FOOT FOOT BELLY
ELBOW
NAILS TOES PADS

Pet Your Parts. Make finding your kid's body parts a singsong game.
"Ears. Abby, touch your ears.
Nose. Abby, touch your nose."

When the dog or cat is in a patient mood, include it in the game.
"Touch your nose, now kitty's nose.
Touch your toes, now kitty's toes.
Touch your tail, now kitty's tail."

Kitty, wait!

NICE KITTY

Just because an animal is a pet doesn't mean it's harmless. Show your child how to approach pets with the same care they would give a wild creature. When you meet a dog on the street, you might say to the owner, "May my child touch your dog?" Hold out your hand with the palm down. Let the dog sniff. If the animal seems friendly and ready for more contact, go ahead slowly. A gentle "Hello" allows both your child and the pet to feel relaxed and secure.

★ BUGS? ★

Look, a bug! Kids tend to call any small critter a bug. Look closer. Count the legs. It may not be a bug at all. Does it matter if your kid knows the correct name? Not really. Learning to be a good observer is what counts.

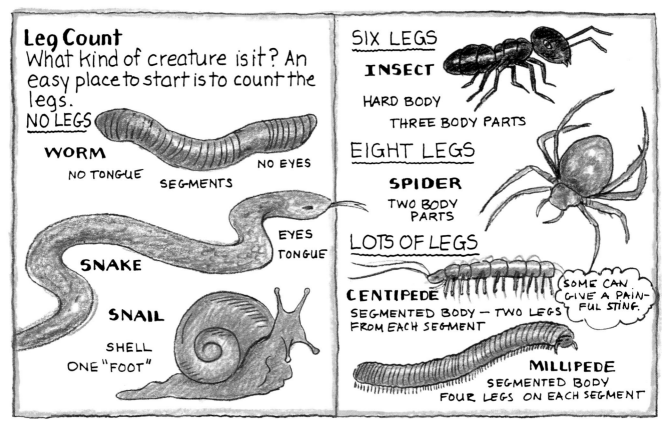

Leg Count
What kind of creature is it? An easy place to start is to count the legs.

NO LEGS
WORM
NO TONGUE
SEGMENTS
NO EYES

SNAKE
EYES
TONGUE

SNAIL
SHELL
ONE "FOOT"

SIX LEGS
INSECT
HARD BODY
THREE BODY PARTS

EIGHT LEGS
SPIDER
TWO BODY PARTS

LOTS OF LEGS
CENTIPEDE
SEGMENTED BODY — TWO LEGS FROM EACH SEGMENT

SOME CAN GIVE A PAINFUL STING.

MILLIPEDE
SEGMENTED BODY
FOUR LEGS ON EACH SEGMENT

Bug Box. A clear plastic box with a magnifying lid is a great tool for little kids. It captures wiggly specimens and is inexpensive. The larger size is best for small hands.

Magnifiers let you take a really close look. A medium-quality, fairly large magnifying lens is easiest for young kids to use. The cheap ones are dim, fuzzy, and they don't enlarge enough to be interesting.

★ PILL BUGS ★

These common little creatures are good animals for kids to touch because of their tough outer skeletons. But do take care: their legs break easily. These questions work on any wild creature your preschooler might meet.

Find them in damp places. Look under logs and leaf litter in flower beds or forest floors. Make searching for creatures part of the process. Ask your child's help:
"Could we find roly-polies on the roof? Where do you think we should look?"

Things to Look For:
- How many legs? Is it an insect?
- How does it move?
- What does it do to protect itself?
- Can you find the eyes? Mouth? Feelers?
- What do you think it eats?
- See any babies? (They are the smaller ones.)

Things to Know:
- Sow bugs run when they are scared, but pill bugs roll up in a ball.
- Pill bugs are crustaceans. Like their lobster cousins, they must live in damp places.
- They scavenge a diet of rotting plants. Scavengers are recyclers of plant litter.
- If your child is interested, check out a book to find out more facts.

ANATOMY
— ANTENNA
SETS OF LEGS
PLATES ON BACK (ECTO- SKELETON HARD SHELL)
TAIL

Lookit, Mommy! I see one, two, three under this big stick!

★ WILD KINGDOM ★

Here are a few small critters common to many neighborhoods. All are safe for a child to handle. Reinforce gentleness. A crushing encounter can be devastating for a child as well as a snail. Here are some things to notice:

EARTHWORMS

LADYBUGS

Find them on green plants near aphids in warm weather.

Things to Notice
- Count the legs.
- They play dead when on their backs.
- There are many kinds. Some have different marks like the "two-spotted" and "nine-spotted." "What kind did you find?"

Things to Know
- Because ladybugs eat juicy aphids, gardeners love them.

Find them in moist soil where plants are rotting. Night is best. Be careful. Their soft bodies are easily broken.

Things to Notice
- Tiny "whiskers" on their undersides help them grip the ground.
- Rings. Count them. Old worms have more than 100.
- Wide saddle (clitellum) is toward the front of the worm.
- Can you see its mouth? You'll need a magnifier.
- Earthworms have no eyes. But they are sensitive to light all over their bodies. Vibrations scare them.

Things to Know
- Cut a worm in half, and it will grow into two worms.

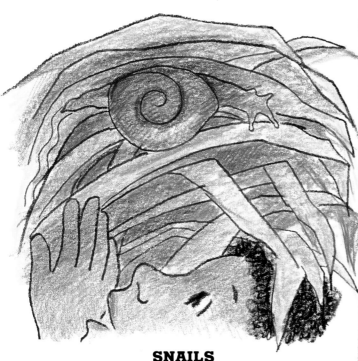

SNAILS

Find them where the ground is damp and plants are thick. Look for silvery trails. Careful! Snails have fragile shells. If they break, the animal will die.

Things to Notice
- Snails have two sets of feelers. The short ones are smellers. The long ones are the snail's eyes. A snail can see light and dark.
- Set the snail in a glass. Looking from underneath, you can see its mouth.
- Watch how it moves on its one "foot."

Things to Know
- Snails have 18,000 teeth on their tongues.
- Snail Trails. Dip the snail's foot in food coloring, set the snail on paper, and watch it make a track across the page.

Looking at Critters. These questions work on any critter—worm or wombat. Remember to use as many of your sensing tools as you can:

- What do you see?
- Is it like anything else?
- How does it move? Does it crawl? Slither?
- Can you count its legs?
- Is the head separate from the body?
- What color is it?
- How does it feel? Smooth or bumpy?
- Does it smell? Can you smell it?
- Does it make any sounds?

Look, it's crawling. I think it gots a bunch of legs. One, two, three, four— I can't see all of them...

★ ANIMAL HOUSE ★

Can I keep him? It's fine to have a snail spend the night, as long as you treat it right. Making an animal house is a good lesson in thinking about what an animal needs to live and how every critter needs a special habitat.

Capturing Animals. Let your child know animals can get scared, especially when they are taken away from their homes. Tell your child, "It's OK to keep an animal in the house for a short while, if we can keep it safe and healthy. Then we let it go EXACTLY where we found it." "Have you ever been lost or scared?"

Take Care. Creatures are likely to die unless they are returned to their habitats. Keep an animal overnight, or at the most a few days. If you disturb an animal's home when looking, remind your child to return rocks, logs, and leaves just as he found them. ("You wouldn't want somebody leaving the roof off your house, would you?")

Animal House. Here are two simple ways to create a critter cage for wild guests like snails or ladybugs.

1. Poke holes in glass jar lid.

2. plastic lids

rolled up screen piece

Now you can put in some nice, squishy leaves.

This is a very cozy house.

Furnish the House. What does the animal need to survive? Take a good look at where you found it. Try to duplicate the habitat. What does the animal need to live? To eat? To drink? To feel safe?

She needs lotsa leaves. Maybe some peanut butter, too.

Keeping Pill Bugs. Add a layer of soil. Sprinkle soil with water (so it's moist but not soggy). Put in some decaying leaves for food. Make a hiding place with sticks and leaves. These bugs hate bright light.

Keeping Snails. Layer moist soil on the bottom of the cage. Make a dark leafy place for the snail to hide in. Feed it lettuce or the green leaves that it was captured on. Keep the cage damp and cool.

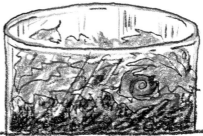

Keeping Worms. Put in several inches of moist but not muddy soil. Add a layer of dead leaves. Add lettuce for food. Remove it if it spoils. Sprinkle the dirt with water drops to keep it damp.

Keeping Ladybugs. These won't live long without a fresh supply of aphids for food. Add a bit of soil, a rock for a hiding place, and plenty of leaves with aphids. No need to keep them wet; juicy aphids provide all the moisture they need.

SCIENCE WORDS: *HABITAT, SOIL, MOIST, DECAYING* **45**

★ SKILLS LIST ★

Whether it's mud pies or playing with magnets, preschoolers are constantly learning about how the world works. Each activity helps them to develop a core set of skills and concepts. The notes at the bottom of every activity page in this book list the skills in that activity. These skills are defined below for your learning pleasure.

Experimenting and Testing: Testing actions and their results is a basic activity for young children. "I hit Sam, so he hit me back." Scientific thinking is a more formal approach to the testing that kids naturally do. These are the steps:

1. Observation. Often observations take the form of a question. "How come your socks stink?"

2. Prediction (or making a hypothesis). This is guessing why or having a theory. "Not all my socks—just the dirty ones."

3. Experimenting (or testing). Checking a guess or hypothesis. "Let's give the sniff test to a pile of clean socks and a pile of dirty socks."

4. Conclusion. Evaluate the test result. "Only the dirty socks stink. So it must be the dirt that stinks and not the socks."

Communicating: Learning how to express ideas is as important as knowing the names for things. Talking about science offers lots of opportunities for describing the world and how it works.

Comparing and Matching: Identifying like and not alike. "Jana, are these two leaves the same?" "How are those dogs different?"

Conservation: Knowing that the arrangement of things can be changed while their amount remains the same. Count out two equal groups of stones. Pile one up. Stretch the other into a line. Which one has more? Kids who haven't yet grasped this new concept will tell you the line has more (because it looks like more). By the age of eight, children understand that arrangement and quantity are separate ideas.

Ordering: Learning to put things in the order of a particular quality, such as color or size. Understanding variations, such as dark to light or big to small. "You made big, medium, and little balls of clay."

Recording: Making a record of activities to be remembered later. Drawing, dictation, graphs, and collections are all ways to record. "Anna, do you remember the flower that is in this picture? And where did you see it?"

Transformations, Reversibility: Knowing that things change. Understanding that some processes can be "undone" (such as ice melting) and some things can't (such as a seed sprouting).

Sorting and Classifying: Learning to group things by their properties. Children begin sorting by using one property. "All the yellow ones go into the can." As their skill becomes more advanced, they can sort by using more than one characteristic. "Red bumpy ones go together, and the other red ones go there."

★ INDEX ★

Use this index to quickly find an appropriate activity for wherever you happen to be. Check the Contents at the front of this book for a more complete activity list.

While You Wait
(no preparation needed)
Walk and Talk 7
Whole World Series 8
Pet Parts 39

In the Car
(or traveling anywhere)
Backseat Science 27

In the Bath
Bubble Lab 16
Bathtub Play 18
Float a Boat 20

In the Kitchen
Bubble Lab 16
Juicy Cubes 21
Cooking Up Chemistry 22
Magic Beans 36

On Your Own
(get them started and let them go)
Whole World Series 8
Bubble Lab 16
Sand Play 19
Static Magic 25
Messing with Magnets 26
Marble Mazes 28
Bouncing Beams 30
Seeds, Please! 34

One on One
What Sort Walk 8
Collections 9
Cooking Up Chemistry 22
Messing with Magnets 26
Marble Mazes 28
Shadow Tracks 31
Dandy Dandelions 33
Bugs? 40
Animal House 44

Good for a Group
Walk and Talk 7
Smellers, Shakers, and Feelies 10
Go Blow Air! 14
Float a Boat 20
Cooking Up Chemistry 22
Static Magic 25
Glass Garden 36
Wild Kingdom 42
Animal House 44

Outdoors
Theme Walk 7
Wind Ring 13
Outdoor Bubbles 17
Sand Play 19
Bouncing Beams 30
Shadow Tracks 31
Dandy Dandelions 33
Seeds, Please! 34
Pill Bugs 41
Wild Kingdom 42